# BIG DRIPS
## FROM BATH AND WELLS

HILARY BINDING

ryelands

Originally published by Halsgrove
under the Ryelands imprint, 2008

Text Copyright © 2008 Hilary Binding
Illustrations Copyright © 2008 Jennie Reed

British Library Cataloguing-in-Publication Data
A CIP record for this title is available from the British Library


ISBN 978 0 9556477 9 6


RYELANDS
Halsgrove House
Ryelands Industrial Estate
Bagley Road, Wellington, Somerset TA21 9PZ
Tel: 01823 653777   Fax: 01823 216796
email: sales@halsgrove.com
website: www.halsgrove.com

Printed by The Short Run Press Ltd, Exeter

# CONTENTS

# WHAT'S IT ALL ABOUT?

In 2009 we celebrate 1100 years since the diocese of Bath and Wells was established. In case you are wondering, a diocese is a geographical area made up of lots of parishes and headed by a bishop.

Christians in Celtic Somerset, the time of Carantoc and Decuman, looked for spiritual leadership to a bishop who travelled among them preaching and teaching. The Saxon bishop, in contrast, had a fixed headquarters and for 200 years before 909 the bishop at Sherborne looked after a huge area which included Somerset, Dorset and Wiltshire. In 909 the people of Somerset were given a bishop of their own, Athelm (we'll come across him in the story of Dunstan) and he had his throne, his *cathedra*, at the old minster at Wells.

Over the next 300 years the diocese kept changing its name – first Wells, then Bath, then Bath and Glastonbury and, at last, after a great deal of squabbling, Bath and Wells.

Water, of course, is a key element in both Bath and Wells – healing waters at Bath and fresh, clear, cleansing water at Wells, a reminder of the water of baptism. Plenty of Big Drips!

Some of these stories are founded on legend while others are based on historical evidence. The Alfred Jewel is an archaeological puzzle. There are saints and bishops, schoolboys and choristers, frightened clergy and hungry nuns, young girls and at least one visionary woman. Most may be history but there are plenty of lessons for today, not least in Bishop Peter's story set in the war-torn Holy Land of 2008.

# THANK YOU!

Many people have helped me with this book and I would like to thank them all. First and foremost I would like to thank Dr Robert Dunning who has worked with me from the start and has researched and checked most of the stories and given me some really good ideas. Without him you wouldn't be reading *Big Drips* at all.

Thank you to Marcus Capel and pupils from Timberscombe First School who tested some of the stories and gave me lots of hints for improving them. Thanks too to Maureen Bollard, Diocesan Education Adviser, and her team at The Old Deanery for their advice. Michael and Ros Comer told me the story of Bishop Jocelin and they may even recognise some of their phrases in the text.

I'm sure you will love the drawings in this book. Thank you Jennie for your imaginative ideas and hard work getting the pictures completed from my notes before you left for your Gap!

Many thanks to David Brown for drawing the timeline under pressure and thank you too to Jenny, to many of my friends at Heritage Services, especially Tom Mayberry for commenting on the text, my publisher Steven Pugsley and anyone else who helped with information or advice or listened patiently as I tried out ideas.

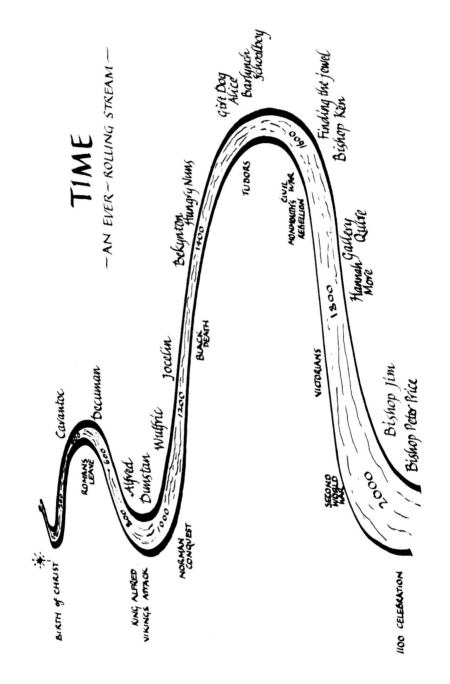

# TIME
## — AN EVER~ROLLING STREAM —

BIRTH OF CHRIST

Cavantoc

ROMANS LEAVE

300

600

800

Documan

Alfred

1000

Dunstan

KING ALFRED
VIKINGS ATTACK

Wulfric

Jocelin

1200

NORMAN
CONQUEST

BLACK
DEATH

Bekynton

1400

Hungry Nuns

TUDORS

MONMOUTH'S
REBELLION

CIVIL
WAR

1600

Gift Dog
Alice

Barlynch
Schoolboy

Finding the jewel
Bishop Ken

VICTORIANS

1800

Hannah
More

Gallery
Quire

SECOND
WORLD
WAR

2000

Bishop Jim

Bishop Peter Price

1100 CELEBRATION

# A STORY FROM OUR BISHOP

Bishop Peter was visiting the Holy Land, the place where Jesus was born. Sadly, many of the people living there were quarrelling and fighting with each other. Both groups of people were afraid of each other. One of the sides was stronger than the other and so they built a big high wall to keep those they were afraid of, out.

The Bishop went through a hole in the wall to visit the people on the other side. Many houses were damaged. Some had been bombed. People were sad and angry.

The Bishop visited a school. The children were playing football and they invited the Bishop to join in. When they had finished their game they asked him to come and see their paintings. In the paintings were pictures of tanks and guns and bombs. People were lying on the ground. Some pictures showed blood, too.

In the corner of one picture someone had drawn the sun. The sun had a face but it was not smiling; in fact tears were falling from the sun on to the children below.

In the picture was a dove. The Bishop asked what the dove meant. One of the children said, 'It's a dove of peace.' Then the Bishop noticed that the dove had been shot and was falling. He asked again what the dove meant. The children said, 'War and fighting kill our hope for peace.'

The children gave the Bishop a flower. It was red, like blood. 'Thank you,' said the Bishop, 'it's a lovely gift. You are beautiful children. God loves you. I will do all I can to work and pray for peace here.'

The Bishop began his journey back through the hole in the wall. At one place he stopped. He took the red flower, red like blood, and going up to the wall placed it into a crack.
A few moments before, a woman had stepped up to the wall. She, too, had a flower. It was white. Together the Bishop and the woman placed their flowers into the cracks in the wall. The woman said, 'I pray for peace. My white flower symbolises peace.' The Bishop said, 'I pray for an end to bloodshed. My flower symbolises all innocent blood.'

Together they walked through the wall. They told their story to as many people as they could on the other side of the wall. Some people listened and said they, too, had suffered, and that the wall should stay. Some people said, 'Jesus came to break down the walls that divide people, and we must do the same.' Everybody said they would pray for peace.

Now, at home in his chapel in Wells, the Bishop prays for peace.

So can we all.

# THE TALE OF CARANTOC
# AND THE SERPENT

It was the middle of the day but as dark as if it were the middle of the night. A thick, black cloud of acrid smoke hung over the little village and the nearby fields were full of smouldering stubble. Men and women and children stood in small groups watching the flames. Some were crying. Some were frightened. Some were very angry.

A huge, slimy serpent had come out of the marsh and with its loathsome breath had set fire to their crops. Then it had crawled back into its lair. It was not the first time that this had happened and the villagers did not know what to do. If it went on they would have nothing to eat in the winter.

'We must send for the young princes, Arthur and Cato,' said one man. 'They'll know what to do.'

So a messenger was sent immediately up to the castle to ask Arthur and Cato for help.

Soon the two princes came galloping down the hill. They dismounted and began to walk briskly along the seashore assessing the damage. They could see the marsh where the serpent lived but they had no idea how they could tame it. It seemed far too large to tackle with swords and spears but that's what they might have to do.

As the waves lapped at their feet Arthur's eye was caught by a large piece of pink marble that had been washed up by the tide.

'That would make a fine table,' he thought. He called for his servants and ordered them to carry the heavy marble slab up to the castle.

Arthur then turned to the villagers. 'This can't go on,' he said. 'Cato and I will come down with our best warriors tomorrow and we will defeat the serpent.' As they remounted to ride back up the hill the villagers shook their heads and looked doubtful. They didn't believe that even princes with swords could kill this serpent.

Back at the castle Arthur ordered his men to polish up the piece of marble he had found. 'I shall eat my supper off it tonight,' he said. But when the food was placed on the marble in front of him, the slab reared up and all the meat and vegetables and gravy were thrown on to the floor. The table seemed to have magical powers. Arthur was not at all pleased. Tomorrow he would try again.

The next morning, very early, Arthur and Cato and some of

their finest warriors marched down from the castle and took up their positions on the shore. The mist was rising from the marsh and there was a strange bubbling sound. The serpent was waking up.

Suddenly a stranger appeared on the shore. He was walking slowly and looking into the water.

'Can we help you, Sir?' asked Arthur. 'Are you lost?' The stranger was wearing a long gown which made Arthur think he must be a holy man.

'Thank you,' the man replied. 'My name is Carantoc. I have come from Wales across the water in a coracle. Before I set out I threw my marble altar into the sea because God had told me that where it washed up I should make my home and care for the people. I wonder whether you have seen it?'

'I certainly have,' said Arthur. 'I found it yesterday and took it home thinking it would make a fine table. But it throws everything that is put on it to the floor. Now I understand why!

'You can have it back and gladly if you will help us.'

'I will if I can,' said Carantoc. 'You do look as if you have problems,' he added, looking round at the burnt fields.

'There's a serpent that lives in the marsh over there,' said Arthur. 'Every so often it emerges, burns our crops and steals our cattle. If you can help us get rid of it I will give you anything you desire.'

'And look! Here it comes now!' cried Cato.

With a mighty heaving, roaring and hissing and a terrible smell which made everyone hold their noses, the serpent emerged out of the mist, huge and green and slimy. It opened its great mouth and puffed out foul breath and a few sparks in warning. The princes and their warriors bravely drew their swords.

The serpent began to move forward, tossing its head from side to side. Flames poured from its mouth. Everybody, except Carantoc, drew back. Even the princes were terrified!

'Leave this to me,' said Carantoc. He stepped forward and stretched out his hand to the serpent. Then he prayed and asked God to tame the beast. And to everyone's amazement the serpent came quietly up to Carantoc, lowered its head and made a strange mooing sound. Carantoc looped his stole

around the serpent's neck and led it past the cheering villagers up to the castle.

Everyone crowded into the great hall.

'Find the beast something to eat,' said Carantoc. 'It's because it is so hungry that it destroys your crops. It's looking for food!'

'But it can't be trusted,' cried Cato. 'We should kill it.'

'Kill it! Kill it!' cried the villagers.

'No,' answered Carantoc. 'Strange though it may seem, it is one of God's creatures. It won't hurt you any more. Just make certain it has enough to eat!'

And sure enough the serpent went back to its home on the marsh and was given lots of grass and vegetables and a little meat and never caused trouble again.

Arthur and Cato were absolutely delighted. 'You must have your altar back at once and we shall give you some land where you can live.'

Carantoc stayed happily in the village. He cared for the villagers especially those who were old and ill. The children loved listening to his stories. Soon people were baptised and a little church was built and it was always known as Carantoc's church. The village was named Carhampton.

# THE TALE OF DECUMAN AND DAISY

Did you know that there are nearly 500 parish churches in the Bath and Wells diocese? Each one has its own special saint. The churches are often known by the name of their saints like St Mary at Bridgwater, St Peter at Evercreech and St Barnabas at Queen Camel. The cathedral in Wells is named after St Andrew. Do you know the name of your church's special saint?

A few churches are linked with saints who visited England before most people had become Christian. One of these was St Decuman of Watchet.

Decuman was born near the sea at a place called Rhoscrowther in Pembrokeshire in Wales. *(You can find it on a map of Wales near Milford Haven.)* His parents were wealthy and important people and they sent him away to a school where he learned to read and write and was taught about God the Creator.

When Decuman grew up he decided that he didn't want to live in a grand style any more. Instead he wanted to live a quiet and simple life praying and thinking about God. His parents were probably very surprised but they let him do what he wanted.

Nearby at Pwllcrochan there were some men, each living a simple life alone. Decuman went to join them. He chose a spot a short way away from the others and built a small hut out of wood and stone and thatch. He was very happy tending his garden and looking after his cow who was called Daisy. The cow provided milk to drink and to make into cheese to accompany the bread Decuman baked for himself. He spent most of the time talking and listening to God. Some days he joined the other men to hear their leader preach about God and to share bread and wine.

Sometimes people came to talk to Decuman and asked him why he lived all alone in this way. He tried to explain that in this quiet place he felt very close to God. Some people listened carefully and took note of what Decuman said but others just laughed at him and brought their friends to laugh as well. It was time for him to move on.

One man who came to see Decuman was already a Christian. His name was Conan and he was a sailor. He had crossed the sea to Britain several times with cargoes of grain and animal skins.

'They could do with someone like you across the channel,' Conan said. 'One place I visited was called Watchet and the people there have never heard about Jesus. They seemed a pretty rough lot!'

Decuman thought and prayed very hard about what his friend had told him. He decided that God was calling him to go across the sea to Watchet and preach to the people there. He waited eagerly for Conan to visit him again so that he could ask his advice about the journey.

'You'll need to make a strong raft. When you set off keep to the coast until you reach Caerdydd [Cardiff] and then the journey across the water is quite short. I'll stay and help you build the raft. I don't think you know anything about boats!'

'That's true,' said Decuman. 'But there's just one thing, Daisy has to go with me!'

His friend thought he was mad but Decuman insisted. 'She will provide me with milk wherever I am. And who knows whether they have cows in Watchet!'

So the raft had to be sturdy enough for two!

When the raft was finished Decuman gathered up his few possessions – his cross, his cloak, his knife and his milk-bucket – and Conan helped him launch the raft and waved him goodbye. 'God go with you,' he cried as the raft disappeared out of sight.

It was a scary journey but Decuman knew that as he was doing what God wanted, God would protect him. Every evening they pulled into the shore so that Daisy could find some grass and fresh water. One day the waves were quite rough and Daisy was seasick. Decuman was really worried about her. But soon they reached Caerdydd and when they struck out across the wide channel of water, the sea became calm and before long the tide was carrying the raft to the shore.

Decuman landed on the coast where the beach was quite pebbly. It was hard for Daisy to walk on the stones. In the distance Decuman saw some round houses built from stone and thatch with smoke rising from them. Several small boats were pulled up onto the beach. Decuman saw a young boy fishing and asked him the name of the place. 'This is Watchet,' the boy replied proudly. God had guided him straight to the right spot.

Decuman needed to find a place to be on his own. He climbed the hill through the woods and out of the village until he found a grassy space near a spring. This was ideal for Daisy. Most of the people were friendly. They brought him things to eat and drink and one man helped him to build a shelter. He set up a cross, made from two branches, and soon people began to climb the hill to hear Decuman preach. Some decided to become Christians and were baptised.

But there was one man who hated Decuman. He believed in the old gods and thought that Decuman's stories of a loving and forgiving God were rubbish. He didn't like Decuman using the water from the spring for baptising and healing people. He said it was where offerings used to be made to the old gods who were very angry.

One day, as Decuman was saying his prayers, his enemy crept up behind him, raised his sword and cut off Decuman's head. For a moment the blood poured out of Decuman's neck but it suddenly stopped. God – and Decuman – could not be got rid of that easily!

Decuman staggered to his feet and, raising his hands, realised his head had disappeared! What could he do? He knelt down and felt about on the grass. Was this a stone he had found? No surely this was his nose and this furry stuff was his hair!

He picked up his head carefully, took it to the spring and washed it clean. Then he placed it back on his neck and all was well. Or so the story goes…!

Decuman continued to preach and teach the people of Watchet about God's love. Soon a small church was built and later people remembered the old stories about Decuman and he became the church's special saint.

# THE PUZZLE OF THE ALFRED JEWEL

## Finding the Jewel

The church clock struck noon. Although the sun was shining it was a bitterly cold day and Harry was tired of picking up stones. He had already filled his basket five times, his back ached and he was hungry. Just a few more stones and the basket would be full enough to take back to the farmyard at Parker's Field to be checked.

Why he couldn't just throw the stones in the hedge he didn't know. Mr Randall had to be sure that he, Harry, was working really hard all the time.

Harry threw a few last stones into the basket, stood up and stretched. As he bent to pick up the basket he saw something glinting. 'That's a strange stone,' he thought as he reached for it.

The 'stone' was about the length of his middle finger and an odd oval shape. As he started to rub the mud off with his shirt tail he realised that it wasn't a stone at all. It was metal and the colour of the sun! Perhaps it was gold! When he turned it over he could see on the other side a picture of a man coloured in blue and green! Was it a brooch that someone had lost?

Harry started to run to the farm. Then he stopped. 'Better take the basket,' he thought. 'I shall only have to come back for it!'

A tall man came out of the stable. 'What's the hurry, Harry?' he asked. 'Fraid someone's going to eat your share of the bread and cheese!'

'No, Mr Randall. Just look what I've found!'

The farmer took the jewel out of Harry's muddy hand.

'Goodness, boy. I wonder who's dropped that. After dinner I'll take it over to show Sir Thomas. He'll know what to do. And if you clean yourself up, you can come too! You've worked hard these last few days.'

After a meal of bread and cheese washed down by cider, Harry – cleaned up! – and Mr Randall made their way to the big house at Petherton Park. They knocked on the back door and Mrs Giles, the housekeeper, came bustling to welcome them. She was a stout, red-faced woman, full of smiles.

'Why, Francis,' she said. 'What brings you here in the middle of the day? And young Harry? No trouble, I hope!'

'No Mrs Giles. It's just something Harry found in the fields. I want to show it to Sir Thomas. It may be valuable and it's his land.'

'Sir Thomas is in the library. I'm sure he'll be glad to see you.'

They followed Mrs Giles through a large hall with dark wooden panelling and paintings on the walls. A door stood ajar letting a shaft of sunlight into the hall. Mrs Giles knocked and went straight in. 'Francis Randall to see you, Sir Thomas, and young Harry.'

'Come in Randall. All's well I hope. And your mother, Harry? Is she keeping well?'

Harry nodded his head; it was as if his tongue was tied in a knot, but Sir Thomas Wroth spoke kindly and smiled at him.

Then Francis Randall showed him the jewel. Sir Thomas took it over to the window and examined it carefully. 'This is really old,' he said. 'And so beautiful! I must take it over to my Uncle Nathaniel Palmer at Fairfield. He knows about these things.

'Thank you Harry for being so observant and so honest.'

And Sir Thomas felt in his pocket and brought out a gold half sovereign. 'For you, Harry, as a reward. Mr Randall will keep it for you until you are older!'

And Harry just managed to squeak, 'Thank you sir!'

## About the Alfred Jewel

The jewel that Harry found is now known as the Alfred Jewel. It is one of the most famous objects surviving from Anglo-Saxon England. It was discovered in 1693 at North Petherton. We don't know who found it. The story about Harry is just my idea of what might have happened.

North Petherton is just four miles from Athelney where King Alfred took refuge from the Vikings in 878. It is where he is supposed to have burnt the cakes!

Sir Thomas Wroth took the Jewel to his uncle, Colonel Nathaniel Palmer of Fairfield, near Stogursey. Colonel Palmer showed it to friends and scholars who were interested in archaeology. They wondered whether it had been a brooch or part of a necklace or even part of the crown jewels.

The Jewel is unique. It consists of a gold frame around an enamel design which is covered by rock crystal. Around the edge are the words in Anglo-Saxon, AELFRED MEC HEHT GEWYRCAN which means 'Alfred ordered me to be made'. It is almost certain that this was King Alfred.

The Jewel has a socket at one end in the form of an animal head so maybe it was originally mounted on a thin rod, perhaps made of wood or bone. Many scholars now think that it was the handle of a pointer (aestel) for pointing to the words when reading from a book. Books were handwritten and very precious so you didn't cover them with greasy fingerprints. (Well you wouldn't do that today, would you?)

Alfred was very interested in promoting learning. He also established a number of monasteries where books would have

been copied and read. He gave an aestel (pointer) to each of these monasteries.

If this Jewel was the handle of an aestel how was it found in a field at North Petherton?

Did it belong to the abbey at Athelney? When the abbey was closed in 1538 and its property removed was it in a bag of gold that was carried away? Did somebody drop it as they rode through the park at Petherton?

Or was this aestel the property of Alfred himself? Did he lose it while hunting in Petherton Park?

We shall probably never know who it belonged to but what do you think? *You could write your own story of how the aestel was lost.*

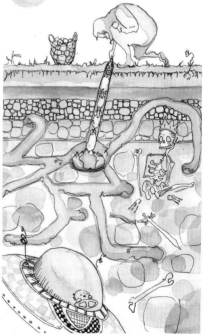

Jennie, our illustrator, has shown how she thinks the Jewel was buried and then brought to the surface again by moles.

If you want to see the Jewel it is in the Ashmolean Museum in Oxford. Sir Nathaniel Palmer bequeathed it to the University of Oxford because it was thought at the time that King Alfred had founded the University.

This means that we can't see it here in Somerset but we know the Alfred Jewel really belongs to us!

# THE TALE OF DUNSTAN AND THE DEVIL

When Dunstan was born at Baltonsborough, three miles from Glastonbury, round about 909, his mother, Cynethryth, told her friends that her son would become a saint.

'Yes dear,' her friends said, shaking their heads. 'We all think our children will grow up to be perfect!'

But a miracle had happened to Cynethryth when she was expecting her baby. She and her husband, Heorstan, had been in church on the Feast of Candlemas. It was an evening service of lights and everybody was holding a candle. Suddenly all the candles were blown out! Everyone was startled and no one knew what to do. There were no matches in those days! Then they all saw a flame of fire descend on Cynethryth's taper and everyone was able to relight their candles from her light.

Cynethryth was sure that this was a message from God showing that her son would be a 'minister of eternal light' to the church in England.

And she was right, for Dunstan grew up to become the friend and adviser of kings and bishops. He became Abbot of Glastonbury and eventually Archbishop of Canterbury. In 1029 he was made a saint.

At the time that Dunstan was born, Glastonbury was rather like an island surrounded by sluggish rivers and very flat land that was often under water. His family were important local landlords and had links with the royal family who had a palace at Cheddar not very far away.

While he was still a small boy, Dunstan's parents sent him to school at the abbey at Glastonbury with a nurse to take care of him. He had to travel by boat to get there. He loved learning and was very talented with his hands – painting and lettering and working in wood and metal. But it was not long before Dunstan became very ill with a severe fever and everyone thought he was going to die. One night he was delirious and, leaving his bed, climbed on a workman's ladder to the very top pinnacle of the abbey church. It was a miracle that he didn't tumble off but climbed down again and fell asleep between two monks. In the morning he didn't remember anything about his adventure!

Dunstan's uncle, Athelm, who was archbishop of Canterbury, heard how talented the boy was and when he was about twelve Athelm sent for him. He began to work as a page in the archbishop's household but before long his uncle arranged for him to move to King Athelstan's court where he continued his education and began to train as a courtier. Quite often the court stayed at Cheddar so Dunstan wasn't too far from home. He continued to study whenever he could and was so honest and open that he soon became a favourite with the king. This made the other courtiers very jealous and they began to spread lies about him saying that he practised black magic. Eventually even the king began to believe the lies and so Dunstan was sent away.

This wasn't enough for his enemies. They went after him, caught him and tied him up and gagged him and threw him into a stinking cesspit. Dunstan thought he would drown but managed to pull himself out of the mire and crawl to the house of a friend. When he had recovered from the shock he made his way to Winchester where the bishop, another relative, welcomed Dunstan into his own house where he was nursed and cared for until he was better.

The bishop tried to persuade him to become a monk, but at first Dunstan wasn't keen. He thought he would like to get married and have children and if he were a monk he couldn't do that. Then he became very ill again, this time with swollen lumps all over his body. Some people thought it was leprosy but it was probably blood poisoning caused by being beaten and thrown in the sewer.

When he recovered Dunstan changed his mind. He decided that God did want him to become a monk and that his illness was a way of telling him so.

Dunstan became a priest in 943 and went to live on his own as a hermit. He built a very small room for himself beside the old church at Glastonbury. It was said to be less than two metres long and just one metre wide so there wasn't room enough to swing a cat! Here he studied books from the abbey library and worked at his crafts.

Dunstan was skilled at working in gold and silver as well as being a farrier and blacksmith. He made little bells for use in church and copied and illustrated beautiful books. In one picture he drew himself lying at the feet of Christ. He wrote above the picture: 'I pray thee, Christ, protect me, Dunstan.' He was very musical and played the harp and sang and also wrote poetry.

There is a famous legend that tells us that while Dunstan was living at Glastonbury the Devil came to tempt him. The Devil was apparently very angry because Dunstan was preaching and spreading the gospel of Jesus with great success. One day, the Devil disguised himself as a beautiful young girl and visited Dunstan who was working in the blacksmith's forge.

The Devil laughed and joked and tried to flirt with the saint but Dunstan did not even look up from his hammering.

Then the Devil started to dance and prance around the room and eventually threw his billowing skirts so high in the air that his hooves could be seen peeping out. At that Dunstan took a large pair of red-hot tongs from the blazing fire, turned suddenly and clamped them hard on the Devil's nose. His screams could be heard from three miles away as he unfurled his wings and shot up into the sky in agony.

Ever since then the tongs have been one of St Dunstan's symbols.

> St Dunstan, as the story goes,
> Once pull'd the devil by the nose
> With red-hot tongs, which made him roar,
> That he was heard three miles or more.

In 940, the new king, Edmund, summoned Dunstan to his court at Cheddar and made him one of his ministers. Edmund trusted Dunstan and often asked for his wise advice. But once again the other men at court became envious and again plotted to get rid of him. King Edmund, like Athelstan, believed the evil rumours that were put about and eventually decided that he would have to dismiss Dunstan.

The next morning, before he spoke to Dunstan, Edmund thought he would go hunting and he and his retinue rode out into Mendip Forest. The king spied a mighty stag and as he began to give chase at great speed in the direction of Cheddar Gorge, he became separated from his attendants. When the stag reached the Gorge it rushed blindly over the edge of the cliffs, followed by the hounds and at the last moment Edmund realised the danger he was in. As he tried to rein in his horse his life flashed before him and he remembered how badly he had treated Dunstan. He said a quick prayer and promised to make amends if his life were spared. And at that moment his horse stopped on the very edge of the cliff and Edmund was safe.

Thanking God for his escape from almost certain death, Edmund returned to his palace. Here he called for fresh horses and then he summoned Dunstan and together they rode straight to Glastonbury. Entering the church, the king first went to the altar and knelt in prayer. Then he took a bemused Dunstan by the hand, gave him the kiss of peace and seated him on the abbot's throne. 'You are to be the new abbot of Glastonbury,' he said.

Edmund made generous gifts of land and money to both Dunstan and the abbey which had fallen on hard times since

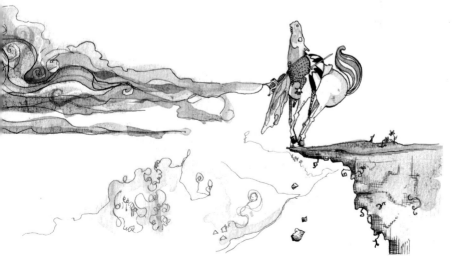

the Vikings attacked in the ninth century. As abbot, Dunstan was able to restore the buildings at Glastonbury and to make sure that the monks were living by the rules as they should.

Later Dunstan became a bishop and was also adviser to several successive kings. He was always outspoken and at one point had to leave the country for a while after he rebuked King Edwy for living immorally. He was eventually made Archbishop of Canterbury by the next king, Edgar.

As archbishop, Dunstan worked hard for the well being and peace of his people. He established schools and loved to teach the boys in the cathedral school at Canterbury himself. He built and restored several churches including All Saints and St Dunstan's at Stepney in London. The 'bells of Stepney' in 'Oranges and Lemons' belong to this church that he built.

Dunstan died at Canterbury in 988 but he was always remembered afterwards at Glastonbury where he had been abbot. Many people went there as pilgrims to pray at his shrine. In 1988 people came from all over the world to mark Dunstan's death a thousand years before. They all belonged to churches and parishes dedicated to St Dunstan.

# THE TALE OF WULFRIC AND OSBERN

My name is Osbern and my father, Brictric, was once the priest here at Haselbury. When one day he asked me if I would like to take on the job of servant boy to our local hermit, Wulfric, I rather liked the idea. I wouldn't have to be working in the fields from morning till night in all weathers. Instead I'd have to run errands and take messages and sometimes be the boy who helped in church when Wulfric took services. I might even meet some interesting people.

Of course I'd have to do the cleaning as well but when your master lives in one tiny room about three metres square, you know there's not going to be too much to do! So I said that I would like to do the job and went off to meet Wulfric to see if I would fit the bill and, I'm glad to say, I did.

Before I took over my father told me a bit about Wulfric's background.

He was born round about 1080 at Compton Martin not long after the Normans conquered England and became our over-lords. Wulfric's family was Saxon but they'd kept their land and had enough money to send him to train as a priest. After he was ordained he went to work as parish priest at Deverill in Wiltshire. It was a small place and he didn't have much to do so he was able to go hunting with his dogs and hawks most days.

Then something happened which changed his life. One day as he was returning from hunting, Wulfric was approached by a 'beggar' dressed in dirty rags. The man held out his hand and asked for a new coin with King Henry I's head on it.

Wulfric was surprised. He was happy to give the 'beggar' money but no one had asked for a particular coin before. He told the man that he wasn't sure whether he had one.

The 'beggar' told him that if he looked in his purse he would find two new silver pennies and a silver halfpenny. So Wulfric looked and there they were, bright and shiny. He immediately gave them to the 'beggar' who thanked him and then told Wulfric that his life was going to change.

Wulfric thought a lot about this encounter. He realised that the man wasn't really a beggar but a messenger from God. From then on he began to pay more attention to his prayers and to reading the Bible. He looked after the people of Deverill and didn't go hunting or to parties any more.

When William FitzWalter, the Norman lord of the manor of Compton Martin, heard what had happened he invited Wulfric to go to Compton as the parish priest. Wulfric was glad to do so. He lived comfortably with the FitzWalter family in the new stone manor house and shared their meals. He visited the sick and elderly, taught the children and spent long hours in the church praying and listening to God.

Ten years later Wulfric decided that God wanted him to do something new. He wanted him become a hermit so Wulfric asked for a cell or room where he could live simply on his own.

A cell was built for him here at Haselbury. It's attached to the church on the north side of the chancel. There's a doorway into the church so that Wulfric can go in to say mass and to pray. But there's no door on the outside, just a small arched opening so that Wulfric can talk to people and receive food. A small window high up near the roof lets the light in.

Once Wulfric had decided that I was the right boy to be his servant I moved in to a small room which was attached to his cell. This meant that I was always on hand if he wanted me for anything.

Wulfric lived a very simple life. After saying mass in the morning he would spend the day praying or reading or just thinking about God. He didn't have a chair so he read standing up, propped against the wall. Each night he only slept for a few hours and he ate practically nothing.

The monks over at Montacute provided Wulfric's food. Sometimes I had to fetch it. It was quite a walk but I enjoyed getting out and about and seeing how many different birds and butterflies I could spot.

Wulfric ate so little and he often gave what he had away. One day when I'd been to fetch his food I was tempted to keep a loaf of the lovely fresh bread for myself. It smelt so good and I longed to devour it there and then. Instead I hid it in my leather bag to enjoy later.

But in the evening when I came to eat it, all I could find in my bag was a heavy, round stone. I knew I'd done wrong and so I told Wulfric what had happened.

'Bring me the stone,' he said kindly.

I fetched the round stone from my bag and showed it to him. Then Wulfric said a blessing over it and it immediately became a hot, crusty loaf smelling delicious. 'Let's share it,' he said and I knew I was forgiven. I didn't try anything like that again. It seemed to me that Wulfric had special powers and could see what was happening even when he wasn't present.

Take the day, for example, when my mother, Godida, was at home carefully stitching an alb for Wulfric to wear in church. She started to sew a wrong seam in the linen. Wulfric, sensing her mistake from his cell, called for me. 'Osbern,' he cried. 'Run quickly and tell your mother to take care or she'll have to stitch that sleeve again!'

Another time Wulfric shouted to me: 'Osbern! Osbern! Make haste! Old Mother Margaret has slipped and fallen into the duckpond! Run and help her out!' Sure enough when I reached the pond in the middle of the village there was the poor old woman struggling to crawl out of the mucky water and all covered in duckweed.

One day the Montacute monks sent some of their own servants with food and wine for Wulfric. These men, who should have known better, decided to help themselves to some of it. They hid some bread and a jar of wine in the hedge by the abbey gate and planned to collect it on their way back. Then they would enjoy a secret feast!

But when they got back to the abbey and opened up the bundle they found that the bread was full of maggots and there were frogs in the wine jars! Dishonesty certainly doesn't pay!

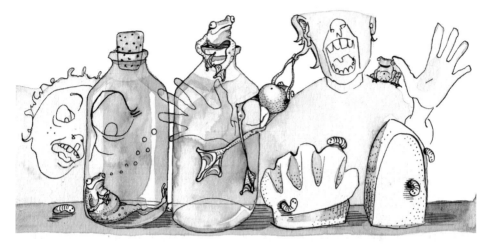

Wulfric was determined to discipline himself and he always wore a hair shirt made out of goatskin. It was so prickly and uncomfortable against his skin. But that wasn't enough. He decided he must wear a heavy tunic made of metal rings over the hair shirt to keep it firmly against his skin so that it would itch even more! When the tunic arrived and he put it on it was so long that he couldn't kneel to say his prayers. The lord, William FitzWalter, offered to send it to London or Exeter to be shortened but Wulfric said it would take too long to do that. William must cut it himself.

Lord FitzWalter said he hadn't the tools to cut through metal but Wulfric asked him to try so he borrowed some strong, sharp shears from the blacksmith and started to cut through the iron rings. Meanwhile Wulfric said his prayers.

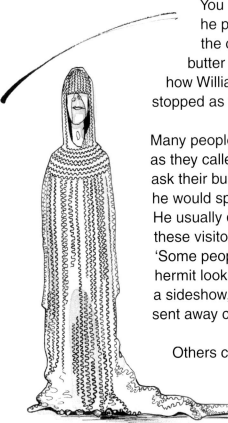

You may not believe this but while he prayed the shears cut through the chainmail like a knife through butter but when he stopped to see how William was getting on, the shears stopped as well. So he kept praying!

Many people came to see the holy man, as they called him. I would greet them and ask their business and then ask Wulfric if he would speak with them.
He usually did. I knew that Wulfric found these visitors tiring. He once said to me: 'Some people only want to see what a hermit looks like and how he lives. I'm not a sideshow, Osbern.' These people he sent away courteously but quickly.

Others came to ask his prayers or his advice and Wulfric would spend many hours talking to them and helping them. I often saw people arrive in tears but when they left they were calm and smiling.

Some people sent presents and generally Wulfric gave these away to the poor of the parish. I remember that once a rich merchant, sure that Wulfric must be cold in winter, sent him a wolfskin cape. Wulfric put it on one side. 'It's far too comfortable for me,' he said.

One snowy day soon after, a poor man came to Wulfric for

help. He had no money and few belongings.

'He shall have the wolfskin cape,' said Wulfric. 'I knew we'd find a good home for it! Bring it quickly, Osbern!'

I fetched the cape but when we opened it up out ran a little mouse. It had nibbled holes all over the back of the cape! When Wulfric saw what had happened he was angry. 'Perish the mouse that has done this!' he cried. The mouse ran across the room to his feet and dropped dead and Wulfric was very sad and wished he hadn't lost his temper.

THE RODENT REVIEW

MYSTERIOUS MOUSE MURDER!
RESIDENT RODENTS UP IN PAWS.

Soon everybody was talking about Wulfric, even at the king's court. When King Henry I heard about the holy man and the many miracles he'd performed his wife, Adelicia, encouraged him to make a visit to Haselbury. They arrived with a large retinue of armed men and beautifully dressed ladies and I was glad that Lord FitzWalter was there to greet them. The king and queen went into the church to speak with Wulfric and I noticed that one of the best dressed of the king's retainers, I think his name was Drogo, stayed by the door into Wulfric's cell. I thought he looked a bit shifty as he whispered to a friend dressed equally grandly in crimson velvet, so I drew closer, eager to hear what he was saying.

To my horror I overheard him say, 'Keep watch! I'm going to search the old fool's cell. It's sure to be full of money and jewels that pilgrims have given him.' And at that very moment he was struck down and lay on the ground, paralysed. When the king heard what had happened he was so angry. 'I didn't realise I was harbouring such a wicked man at my court,' he cried and begged Wulfric's forgiveness.

Drogo was restored to health but was banished from the king's court and never seen again.

As Wulfric grew older he became gaunt and thin and lost much of his strength. He knew when he was going to die and

told me that he wanted to be buried here at Haselbury. Last Sunday he asked me to pray with him and as I knelt beside his hard little bed, holding his wasted hand, I felt his spirit slip away.

When the news of his death reached Montacute the monks came in a grand procession to take his body back to the priory. A great crowd of villagers surrounded the church as I tried to explain that Wulfric wanted to be buried at Haselbury. What happened next was so unseemly. Our dear Wulfric had died and here were people quarrelling over his body. The monks locked themselves into the cell with Wulfric and tried to get the body out by widening the aperture.

Eventually Lord FitzWalter insisted on speaking with the monks and when they had listened to him and seen the crowds that had arrived to prevent them taking the body away they gave in at last to reason. Wulfric was buried at Haselbury and for many, many years a steady stream of pilgrims came to the village to pray at his tomb.

# THE TALE OF BISHOP JOCELIN
# AND THE DRAGON

It was early August and so hot! The sun had been shining brilliantly all day and the weather seemed set fair. In the fields the corn stood upright and golden, ripe and ready to be cut. Tomorrow they would start the harvest.

All the able-bodied men and boys – old and young, fat and thin – from Dinder and Dulcote and North Wootton would meet not long after sunrise and start to cut the barley. Later their womenfolk – mothers, wives and daughters – would join them, tying the stiff stalks into thick bundles and stacking them together to dry.

It looked as if the harvest would be plentiful this year and that meant enough to eat during the winter. Red apples ripened on the trees and the beans were bursting out of their pods. In the fields the young sheep and cattle were plump and healthy and in the woods the pigs snuffled contentedly. In a few weeks many beasts would be slaughtered and their meat salted down to preserve it for the winter.

Work was done for that day and the weary villagers of Dinder had gathered together near the church to gossip over horn beakers of barley beer. The children were playing at hopscotch in the distance at the foot of Worminster Sleight.

The men were talking about their bishop. Bishop Jocelin Trotman had been born at nearby Launcherly and as a young man had been friendly with several of the men of Dinder. The bishop had recently returned from London and on his way back to Wells he'd ridden through the village and stopped to admire the harvest.

'I wasn't surprised when he and his brother went off to train as priests,' said one of the older men. 'Nor that they went into service with our bishops. Their family has always produced priests and Jocelin's grandfather was a trotman. He was always riding here and there with messages from the bishop to the sheriff or the king.

'But I'm amazed at how much he's done since he became bishop. Take the new west front of the cathedral with all those carved and painted figures. We've all seen it when we've been to market in Wells. It'll be magnificent when it's complete.'

'Then there's his new house with its huge hall,' said another, younger, man.

'And what about the park?' interrupted a third, pointing to newly planted woodland surrounded by wooden fencing about half a mile away.

'Well, he needs plenty of game for the table in that new hall of his,' said one of the women. 'If the present king should visit as King John did, Jocelin will need to provide for a hundred or more guests.'

'But the important thing is that he is still Jocelin Trotman,' said the man who had first spoken. 'He knows and cares about ordinary folk. When we meet on the road he always halts and even dismounts for a few words with old friends.'

They refilled their beakers, drank deep and were silent for a while.

All of a sudden there was a strange rumbling sound in the distance. Could it be thunder? Surely the weather wasn't going to break.

The sky began to darken ominously. Anxiously they all turned in the direction of the noise. A huge dark shape like a thundercloud began to emerge from behind Worminster Sleight. For a moment they thought it was a cloud but as they watched they realised that it was a monstrous bird-like creature with huge leathery wings and a body covered in greeny-yellowy scales. As it flew slowly towards them smoke and flames poured from its nostrils.

Then one of the terrified women screamed: 'Our children!'
They could see the children starting to run back towards the
village and all the villagers with one accord ran to rescue
them. But before they could reach them they saw the beast
reach down with one of its wings and gather up a little girl.
Then the dragon, for that's what it was, circled the fields still
breathing out flames and disappeared behind the hill.

'Mary! My Mary!' The little girl's mother was distraught,
weeping and wailing, and her husband hastened to her side to
try to comfort her. But there was nothing that anyone could do
to help. Horrified families clung together, thankful that they
were safe, and wondering what tomorrow would bring.

Early the next morning the men of Dinder, still stunned by
what had happened, stumbled across the blackened cornfields
to Worminster Sleight but there was no sign of little Mary. And
it was clear that much of the wonderful harvest had been
ruined.

Later that day the dragon appeared again, this time over
Dulcote, and once again a child was seized and crops were
burnt. The following day it was the turn of North Wootton.
Here all the children were hidden safely indoors and so the
beast satisfied itself with some of the fat cattle that had been
left grazing in the fields.

The terrified villagers didn't know what to do. The fields
around their villages were devastated and people hardly dared
venture out of doors. In consternation the leaders of the three
villages met. They decided that the only thing to do was to
ask their friend, Bishop Jocelin, for help. So in fear and
trepidation, armed with daggers, staves and cudgels, a group

of village men set out over the blackened fields the short distance to Wells.

It was nearly dark when they reached the Bishop's new house and the servants were busy tending to the horses and barring the doors for the night. A young man, dressed in fine clothes welcomed them into the warmth and safety of the Bishop's hall.

'You certainly seem in some kind of trouble,' he said. 'The women will bring you warm water and cloths so that you can refresh yourselves and I will find the Bishop. I am sure he will want to see you straight away.'

It was only as he left the room that the men looked at each other and realised that their faces and hands and clothes were all covered in black ash. What sights they were and hardly fit to meet a bishop! They cleaned themselves as best they could and the women took their cloaks to shake off the dust out of doors.

By the time Bishop Jocelin appeared they were decent again.

The bishop greeted them like old friends and listened to their desperate story. Then he instructed his servants to give the men some supper and find them somewhere to sleep for the night while he withdrew to his chapel to think and pray.

By early morning Bishop Jocelin knew that he had to confront this dragon himself. He called for his bodyguard who appeared, dressed in chain mail and armed with swords and shields and lances. Jocelin himself wore no armour and carried only his crozier and a sword.

The fields were shrouded in mist as the bishop led his soldiers and the men from the three villages out of the palace and across the moat. As the sun began to rise they turned to the east and took the track that led by the Bishop's park to Dinder. In the air was the acrid smell of burning brought on the breeze from the devastated villages.

The sky before them glowed ruby-red as the great gold sun rose higher in the sky. But suddenly an all-too-familiar shadow appeared on the horizon. Flapping its huge leathery wings the dragon of Dinder drew near and flew overhead, circling the group of men who huddled together and gazed upwards in fear and disbelief.

Perhaps the beast recognised the presence of good in the saintly bishop for it began to screech with anger and rage. Then it swooped rampaging to the ground, burning a field as it fell.

The Bishop stood firm and calm and looked the dragon in the eye.

'Stand back, men, and take cover.  I shall deal with this evil beast myself.'  Then taking his crozier in one hand and his trusty sword in the other he stepped up to the dragon and disappeared into the cloud of fire and smoke that was the dragon's breath.

For a moment nobody could see the bishop.  Some of the men fell on their knees and began to pray.  Then a most terrible scream rent the air round about.

The flames died down, the smoke cleared and there stood Bishop Jocelin, blackened by dragon-fire, weary, worn and triumphant.  Across his feet lay fragments of the monster's head, smouldering still.  And on the ground behind him lay the rest of the dragon, limp and still.

As they stood there excited people from the three villages came running and cheering and thanking God.

'Take the monster away,' said Bishop Jocelin, 'and see that you bury him safely under the dragon hill – Worminster Sleight –

at Wootton. And every fifty years from now until the good Lord Jesus comes a second time, you are, in these three villages, to celebrate the conquering of the dragon. Otherwise it will rise again and steal your children forever.'

The people of the three villages promised they would and to this day there is a dragon celebration every fiftieth year in Dinder, Dulcote and North Wootton.

# THE TALE OF BISHOP BEKYNTON AND HIS JESTER

*There is a tradition that Bishop Bekynton had a jester but we don't know anything about him! These are my ideas about their friendship.*

Do you know what a jester is? I went to a wedding not long ago and we had a jester to entertain us. He sang and told jokes, performed tricks, rode a unicycle and made us all laugh. Back in the 1400s jesters, who were sometimes called fools, often wore red. They had pointy hats, sometimes with two points like donkey's ears. If you look at a pack of cards and find the Joker – the one card that doesn't fit with the rest – you will see he is dressed as a jester.

But jesters were not just jokers telling funny stories like comedians on television. They were often wise and sensible people who were not afraid of speaking the truth.

It seems likely that Thomas Bekynton, who was Bishop of Bath and Wells from 1443 until his death in 1465, had a jester and if you visit Wells Cathedral you can see a sculpture, carved in stone and painted, which may have been him.

Bishop Bekynton was born in Somerset at Beckington just outside Frome in c.1390 and took his name from his birthplace. His father was a weaver. Thomas was a bright boy who, somehow or other, was sent away to school at Winchester College and then went on to New College, Oxford where he studied and became a priest. He entered the service of the king and was given some very important jobs but I have to say that he didn't always do as well as the king hoped!

He always loved Somerset and when he became Bishop of Bath and Wells he was really happy to be back in his home county where he could be himself, a simple weaver's son at heart.

He did have plenty of money and one of the first things he did when he became bishop was to do some building work on the palace. He enlarged the bishop's house and built a grand throne room where he would sit to conduct important business. I like to think that one day when the work was nearly finished he stood with his jester wondering whether to leave the inside walls plain or to decorate them in some way.

'What do you think?' he asked.

Jester scratched his head. 'I think we should have pictures on the walls,' he replied. 'Why not paint some scenes from the Gospels and surround them with flowers to remind us in winter of the Somerset countryside in summer. And don't forget to include Mary Magdalene, she always gets a bad press!'

Bishop Bekynton kept a grand house! Often scholars and playwrights and musicians came to visit him and these were occasions for great feasts. Sometimes there would be fifty or more important guests with a hundred or so servants and they all had to be fed.

The kitchen staff would be rushed off their feet. Huntsmen were sent out to snare pigeons and gulls, curlew and plovers, snipe and quails; a swan was taken from the palace moat; ducks and chicken were killed, a heron and a crane were captured and all were roasted along with venison and pork.

There were eggs and fish and pancakes and pies made with minced meat and dried fruit, seasoned with strong spices brought from the East, not to mention huge loaves of bread, pitchers of wine and casks of beer.

Sturdy trestle tables were laid out in the hall with a long table for the bishop's special guests on a dais at one end of the room. Jester sat at the end of this table. 'No good being a vegetarian,' he commented as dish after dish of roast meat and game were brought to the table.

The Bishop was always concerned for the wellbeing of ordinary people. He realised that while he had access to pure water at the palace the people of the city of Wells didn't. He therefore decided to pipe water from the clear springs in the palace grounds into the centre of Wells so that pure water was available for everyone from a conduit in the market place. Today water still flows through the streets of Wells.

Besides the building work at the palace, the bishop built new houses in the city and also made sure that the palace and its grounds and the cathedral close were enclosed by strong walls. In 1450 a violent rebellion led by Jack Cade broke out in Kent. London was attacked and, nearer home, the Bishop of Salisbury was murdered at Edington in Wiltshire. When the news reached Wells everyone was filled with alarm and it seemed wise to make sure that both the palace and the cathedral close were protected in case of a future attack.

Bishop Bekynton loved magnificent gateways and he built at least three – the Bishop's Eye, the Penniless Porch and the Chain Gate. Some bishops would have had their coat of arms carved on such grand buildings but Bekynton felt that that was showing off.

'What should I do?' he asked his friend.

Jester suggested that the buildings be marked by a simple symbol or badge called a rebus instead.

'Why not turn your name into a badge, my Lord? Bekynton. Beacontun. A beacon and a tun (or barrel).' So he did and the rebus you see here was carved on many of Bekynton's buildings in Wells.

*(Perhaps you could design a rebus from your surname?)*

Of course the bishop had responsibilities across his diocese. One day he sent to Taunton Priory to see what was going on there and found that many of the rules were being broken and the regular timetable of services and work and meals ignored. The canons even entertained visitors in their rooms. The prior was given a list of things to be improved and he was also ordered to make sure the canons had enough bread and cheese to eat!

One day the bishop paid a visit to the cathedral school and came back quite bothered. 'They don't seem to have any table manners,' he said to Jester. 'I shall rewrite the rules.' When he'd finished he read some of them to Jester. 'When boys are having their meals they must cut or neatly break their bread, not gnaw at it or tear it with their nails. They mustn't pick their teeth with their knives. They mustn't drink with their mouths full, and they are not to gobble! If they want anything they must ask for it in Latin.'

'It's all right for you,' said Jester. You went to Winchester College and learnt that 'manners makyth man'.'

The bishop ignored him and read on: 'The boys will sleep in the dormitory, three boys to a bed. Two small boys will sleep with their heads to the head of the bed, an older one to the foot. He has to put his feet between the heads of the two small boys.'

'Let's hope he doesn't have cheesy feet!' said Jester.

Jester would always have been at the bishop's side, ready to give advice, comment on important issues and sometimes entertain the visitors. But I think Jester was also the bishop's friend. Perhaps he was the only person the Bishop could confide in and trust with important secrets.

I think he was the person who pointed out to the bishop that when it rained all the vicars choral arrived in the choir stalls dripping wet! 'If, my Lord, you built a covered way between Vicars' Close and the Cathedral they could get here in the dry!' The bishop built the Chain Gate and the vicars choral were so grateful that they promised to pray for the bishop every time they used the walkway!

Fifteen years before he died Bishop Bekynton had his tomb built. He wanted his friend, Jester, to be buried with him in the same grave but that idea was shocking. A mere jester alongside a bishop!

His tomb is very unusual. It is in two layers. On the top is the bishop's effigy made in painted alabaster and showing him dressed in bishop's robes. Below is his corpse. The idea was to make people think. Imagine the bishop saying: 'I seem like this now, grand and important, but I am in fact ordinary and mortal and shall be brought to dust like everyone else.'

On the beautiful iron railings that surround the tomb, on the side that faces the high altar, there may be a likeness of the jester. He seems quite old – his face is lined and wrinkled. He may have been a crookback, born with one shoulder higher than the other. His hands are stretched out before him, large and capable.

Is it my imagination or is he saying, 'Come, my lord bishop and friend. Let us go to meet our Maker together'?

# STONEMASONS

The people who actually built Wells Cathedral were the stonemasons.

The master mason was a highly skilled craftsman who was architect, builder, designer and engineer all rolled into one. Using only a set of compasses, a set square and a staff or rope marked off in halves, thirds and fifths he was able to design and construct amazing buildings that still stand today, centuries later.

Adam Lock was the master mason when the western half of the nave at Wells was constructed. He died in 1229 leaving a widow, Agnes and a son, Thomas. He was clearly a wealthy man for he owned several houses and land in Wells. A head with beard, flowing hair and mason's cap on a corbel at the NW end of nave may be a portrait of him.

The master mason would have supervised other masons who did the actual carving and laying of stone as well as labourers learning the trade plus carpenters, glaziers and painters also involved in the project. The stones were all carved on the ground before being set in place and scaffolding was used to reach the higher parts of the building. Cranes and pulleys were used to help lift heavy materials.

*You can find out more about building a cathedral on www.bbc.co.uk/history Look for the 'Build an Arch' animation which shows you how arches were built and the 'Wells Cathedral Activity' which shows how the West Front, built at the time of Bishop Jocelin, was once painted in blue and red and gold.*

# THE TALE OF THE TWO HUNGRY NUNS

Isabella shivered as she snuggled down on her straw mattress under the thick woolly blanket. It was four-o-clock in the morning and she had just come back from chapel. At least in this nunnery the first two services of the day were run together. Each night at 2am when she was in a really deep sleep the bell for Matins and Lauds would sound. All the nuns got up quickly, wrapped their habits and cloaks around them and sleepily made their way down the stairs into the chapel. Once the readings and psalms and prayers were over they returned to their beds until daybreak.

It wasn't really any colder than usual but Isabella was so hungry! It was six months now since she had first come to the Benedictine nunnery at Barrow. Her family lived in a village nearby at a large farm rented from John Gurney. Her father, John Poleyns, was a good hard-working man and her mother beautiful though not very strong. When she, Isabella, was born John had been afraid that both his wife and daughter might die and he swore that if they lived he would give his daughter to God to say thank you and so on her fourteenth birthday Isabella joined the nunnery at Barrow.

Isabella was quite happy to become a nun. She loved the tiny church in her village, the services when everyone gathered together and she thought the stories from the Bible were really exciting. When the time came for her to leave her family and friends she was sad but knew they would keep in touch. And in the nunnery she was happy. She helped look after sick people in the infirmary and also learnt to use herbs as medicines. The only problem was that she was always hungry. The poor old nun who did the cooking produced sour bread, lumpy pottage and never flavoured the food with herbs and spices as Isabella's mother did. And there simply wasn't enough to eat.

At dinner that day the food was worse than usual. Her friend, Joan Bozum, who was sitting next to her whispered under her breath: 'I can't bear this any more.' (They were not supposed to talk at meals and the Prioress glared at them.) Later in the day they met in the gardens.

'We shall starve at this rate,' said Joan.

'What can we do?' asked Isabella.

'I have a friend,' Joan answered, 'in a nunnery in Wales at Usk. I am sure the food would be better there.'

Joan and Isabella thought it best not to ask if they might leave. They were certain the answer would be 'no'. So, three nights later, instead of returning to their beds after Matins they crept out of the church door which the villagers used and which was always open, and made haste towards Bristol. Here they begged a lift on a boat bound for Wales. The captain was glad to help the two young nuns especially when Joan explained that they were visiting a sick friend in Usk. Isabella felt uneasy about the lie but Joan said that the end justified the means.

They landed at Chepstow and then took the road eastwards towards Usk. They were welcomed at the nunnery and as guests given a good meal and comfortable beds. But the next day, when they explained why they wanted to stay at Usk, everything was different. They were given lumpy straw mattresses and the food was even worse than at Barrow. There were few young nuns at Usk so Isabella and Joan were expected to do all the heavy work in the garden and in the laundry.

How they wanted to return to Barrow but they'd left without permission and would never be allowed back. What on earth could they do?

What do you think they might have done?

## What happened next?

We don't really know what happened next but we do know that somebody felt so sorry for Isabella and Joan that they told the Pope about them! Perhaps one of the Pope's visitors stopped at Usk and took pity on the girls. The Pope, Boniface IX, was clearly sympathetic. In 1398 he wrote to the prior of Bath Abbey asking him to enquire into the matter. He said that if what Isabella and Joan said was true, then they were to go back to Barrow and even have their old warm rooms over the nunnery parlour. I wonder if they did!

*We know about this because the letter from the Pope to the prior has survived.*

# THE TALE OF THE VICAR
# AND THE GIRT DOG DEW

The church door closed with a loud bang. The vicar heaved a deep sigh of relief. It was the week before Easter and he was worn out.

All the villagers were coming to church to confess the things they knew they'd done wrong and to ask God's forgiveness. He, William Russell, had to listen and advise and give each one a penance – maybe extra prayers to say. Then he would tell them that God had forgiven them.

It was hard to believe all the bad things that were going on in his quiet parish.

One man had stolen two chickens from a friend up the road.

An old woman described the lies she'd told about her son's wife. 'I've always hated her,' the old woman said. 'Taking away my son and giving him ideas!'

A plain young woman with lanky hair and a sulky mouth explained how jealous she was of her pretty cousin.

Worst of all, the farmer's son said that he'd lost his temper and tried to kill one of his father's servants.

'Was it the same everywhere?' wondered William as he blew out the candles and made for the door.

He was tired and hungry. He hoped his housekeeper had made a good supper even though it was Good Friday. No

meat, of course, but maybe a tasty vegetable stew with fresh
bread. Would enjoying supper on Good Friday be wrong?

He locked the church door with the huge, iron key. Why did it
have to be so big? It wouldn't fit in his pocket.

As he turned away he thought he saw a shadow moving
behind the trunk of the ancient yew tree near the church stile.
His heart sank. Was it another messenger from the Abbot of
Glastonbury?

Abbot John Selwood was planning to rebuild part of the
church. He expected William, as vicar of Meare, to raise a lot
of money towards the project from his parishioners. William
liked the church as it was. He wished the powerful abbot
would leave it alone.

Suddenly a huge, black-bearded man leapt out from behind
the tree. It was one of the abbot's servants, John Totyn.

But John was a villager with a grudge of his own. Only that
week William had told him that he still owed some of his tithe –
his payment to the vicar – from last year. He was to be sure to
hand over the first of his fresh vegetables as soon as they
were ready. John was furious. He hoped he'd got away with it!
He was going to get his own back!

John rushed up to the vicar. He was waving a long wooden
pole with an iron spike on the end. He raised it in the air and
began to beat the vicar about the head. 'Take that! And that!'
he snarled.

William threw up his arms to protect his face. A blow fell on

his wrist and blood began
to trickle slowly down his
arm. Then John took a
step back and whistled for
his dog. It was a huge,
fierce greyhound and
William knew that it was
usually muzzled.

'Hey, Dew, garde!'
shouted John in a rough
voice. 'Get him! Get him!'

William was terrified. He
tried to shout for help but
the words wouldn't come
out.

Then the dog was upon
him. It pulled him to the ground but William managed to
stagger up again. Then it pulled him down a second time and
began to gnaw on his arm. William could see the toothmarks
and the blood flowing.

Thank God for the huge church key! William raised his other
arm and hit the dog under its ear with a mighty blow. 'Take
that you horrible girt dog!' he shouted.

And at last the dog whimpered and slunk away. John Totyn
looked at William, sneered and strode off.

Just then the local blacksmith and his apprentice came
running into the churchyard. They'd heard the noise and had

come to find out what was going on. They
found William struggling to get to his feet
with blood pouring from his arm. The
blacksmith, shocked to find the vicar in
this state, hurried to help him.

'What has happened?' asked the
blacksmith. 'Was that John Totyn? Shall
I go after him?'

'Best let him go,' answered
William. 'He's one of
the abbot's men
and must be
reported. I need
justice for this attack.'

The next day the abbot visited Meare. William went to see
him. He explained what had happened and showed him his
bloodstained shirt and torn gown. 'See where the girt dog bit
me!' he cried, pulling back his sleeve to show the marks on his
wounded arm. 'My hand is "foul hurt". The man who attacked
me was your servant, John Totyn. He needs to be punished.'

But the abbot said it wasn't his business and walked away.

How was William to get justice? The local court was run by
the abbot's men in the abbot's name. He'd find no justice
there! What could he do?

William decided to appeal to the Lord Chancellor in London.
The Lord Chancellor at the time was Robert Stillington and
William knew him because he was also the bishop of Bath and

Wells.  Surely he'd be able to make Abbot John Selwood see sense.

## What happened next?

William found the money to pay an official to write a petition in the correct way and a messenger carried it to London.  Then William waited to hear what the Lord Chancellor decided should happen.

We don't know what his decision was.  However it looks as if a settlement was made.  In 1479 the bishop allowed William Russell to move to Doulting, another parish in the abbot's patronage, and the vicar of Doulting came to Meare.  It probably meant that John Totyn escaped punishment but at least William was out of it!  He lived until 1487.

*We know all about this including the name of the 'girt dog' because William's petition has survived.*

# THE TALE OF ALICE AND HER EWE LAMB

I was named Alice after my godmother, Alice St John, who lived in a huge, old house at East Luccombe. I remember visiting her one Christmas with my mother and father. The house was decorated with holly and ivy and mistletoe and there were candles everywhere throwing a glowing light and flickering shadows across the Great Hall. There was so much to eat and drink and lots of music and dancing. Everyone was laughing and joking

I loved my godmother. She was tiny and beautiful and so kind and she always let us children play hide and seek throughout the house. There was just one room where she liked us to be quiet. It was her private chapel in the little room over the entrance porch. Here she would kneel to say her prayers each day. When she grew too ill to walk to the parish church a priest would come to celebrate Holy Communion in the chapel. Sometimes we would sit there together and she would tell me stories about her favourite saints.

I was very sad when my mother told me that my godmother had died. The funeral took place at Luccombe church and there were so many people there. It showed how much she was loved and respected.

Back at the house Alice's will was read. I was really excited when I heard that she had left me a ewe lamb. I knew it would grow and have lambs itself which would produce wool which could be sold.

After the funeral feast I stole upstairs into Alice's old chamber where her four-poster bed still stood. It was almost as if she

was lying there but I knew I was imagining things – it was just the bedclothes.

I crept down to her little chapel and said a quick prayer: 'Thank you God for letting me know Alice – and for the lamb. Amen.'

## FROM ALICE ST JOHN'S WILL

*A feather bed and mattress each to William Kelly, Thomas Hilton and Alice Kelly*

*To Robert Molland her godson 2 ewe lambs, 2 steers, a cow, a pair of sheets and a pair of blankets*

*To Alice Kelly her best beads, best girdle and best covered standing cup*

*To each of her servants, men and women, a cow or a heifer*

*To every godchild a ewe or a ewe lamb*

*6s 8d for a great taper (candle) to burn before the statue of Our Lady*

*To the parson of Luccombe a little silver covered standing cup*

*To Margery Leyborne a pair of sheets, a pair of blankets, a coverlet, a mattress and her little blue girdle*

We know about this because Alice St John's will has survived.

# THE TALE OF THE BARLYNCH SCHOOLBOY

It was just after dawn. The sun was rising, the birds singing and it promised to be a really hot day. William Nicolas trotted up the road from Bampton on his native pony and whistled as he went. He was on his way to the priory at Barlynch for his last few weeks at school.

William's father was a prosperous wool merchant whose weavers produced beautiful, fine woollen cloth that was in great demand. Although his father often met merchants from London at the market in Exeter, he had decided to expand his business. For the last week he had been in London showing samples and patterns of his cloth to the leading merchants in the City. And William, just twelve years old, had gone with him.

They had travelled by ship from Exeter, around the coast and up the River Thames right into London and had moored not far from the great Tower. They stayed in lodgings at the Priory of St Bartholomew at Smithfield in the City where there was a famous hospital.

Every day William went with his father to meet wealthy merchants in their large, comfortable houses. He was amazed at the huge buildings and the crowds of people as well as the number of beggars and the awful smell!

Now he was back in the clean, quiet countryside and looking forward to telling his friends of his adventures.

He reached the great arched gateway to the priory and, jumping down, pulled on the bell rope. The monk who let him in welcomed him cheerily. 'Good to see you back, William,' he smiled. William stabled his pony and taking his saddlebags, hurrled along to the dormltory near the schoolroom where all the boys slept. There was no one there. He was late!

School started so early in the summer, round about six-o-clock! He left his bags tidily, pulled out his notebook and ran quickly to the schoolroom. Entering, he stood quietly just inside the door.

Master David Juyne, the schoolmaster, turned from his desk and looked at him over his spectacles and William hurriedly removed his cap and made his bow.

'You are late, boy, but today,' he said, smiling, 'you are forgiven. This afternoon you can tell us of your visit to London. Meanwhile you can write a Latin sentence or two about it.' William took his seat on the wooden bench and began to write: 'Four days ago I was in London...'

William rather liked Latin. His father was keen for him to enter his business and if he could read and write in Latin he would be able to keep records and manage the accounts. For a time William had thought he might become a priest though not a monk, or canon, as the Barlynch monks were called. William was not so keen on learning Latin grammar and chanting verbs with the other boys but he did enjoy reading Latin poetry and working out what it meant.

Sometimes the boys wrote about everyday things or translated English proverbs into Latin. William especially liked the proverb: 'He that cometh last to the pot is soonest wrathful' because it reminded him of his friend, Roger, who always

seemed to be last at meals and got very cross when there wasn't much pottage left for him.

The day was very hot and the boys were really pleased when Master Juyne let them go early so that they could swim in the cool river that ran close by the priory walls.

That night William fell asleep quickly but it seemed to be only a moment before he was woken by a great commotion in the courtyard below. All the poultry started to squawk and fly about while the geese set up a great cackling sound. Had somebody broken in? Was there a stranger in the yard?

The boys were out of bed in an instant and, poking his head through the window, William could see the shadow of a great dog fox stalking a cock bird. The boys all started to shout and then some of the monks rushed into the yard crying out and waving their arms until they frightened the fox out over the wall. Someone had forgotten to lock up the birds!

Next morning Master Juyne introduced some new Latin words to the boys and asked them to write an account – in Latin – of what happened in the night.

William enjoyed school and knew that he was quite a star pupil. When Master Juyne praised his work he wrote in his notebook, rather boastfully: 'Ego sum bonus puer.' (I am a good boy!)

The hot weather continued and it became very hard to concentrate. One day after their breakfast of bread and weak beer, Roger brought a baby rat into the classroom and let it go. Soon all the boys were laughing and jumping up on the benches out of the way of the rat which was running around frantically trying to find a way out. When Master Juyne came in he found chaos. He took up his cane of birch twigs and banged it down on his desk. Everyone sat down very quietly. No one wanted a beating on their bare bum!

'For this disturbance you will all stay in on Saturday morning and write out Latin sentences.'

This was bad news. The boys usually had no school on Saturday and some went home until Sunday night. But there was no changing Master Juyne's mind. On a brilliant Saturday morning the class had to stay in and copy out again and again:
'While you are young and have the time
Why don't you learn, lest you know no more than a beast?'

After that everyone was very careful to behave properly and keep out of Master Juyne's way.

One thing that William didn't like about school was that he was always so hungry and the meals so plain. There was hardly ever any meat although just once the boys were given a feast of bacon and eggs. Nobody knew why. It was such an event that William wrote about it in his notebook: 'I have ete my belyfull of coloppes (bacon) and egges today.'

The days passed quickly and soon the time came for William to leave school. There was no more talk of him becoming a priest. His visit to London had made him realise that he wanted to become a merchant like his father.

And then it was the last morning. As a treat Master Juyne let the boys play the tongue twister game. Each boy recited as fast as he could: 'Three grey greedy geese, flying o'er three green greasy furrows, the geese was grey and greedy, the furrows green and greasy.' Someone always got muddled and soon the class was aching with laughter.

Master Nicolas arrived at mid-morning to take William home. William fetched his bags and saddled up his pony and all the canons came out to wish him well.

'Not a bad lad, Master Nicolas,' said Master Juyne drily as he said goodbye.

Master Nicolas smiled at his son and then they mounted, spurred their horses on and cantered away.

*We know about William and his schoolwork because some of the pages of his notebook have survived in the Somerset Record Office and have been published by Professor Nicholas Orme in the Proceedings of the Somerset Archaeological and Natural History Society.*

# THE TALE OF BISHOP KEN
# AND YOUNG THOMAS

Thomas stood silently, hand-in-hand with his father, John, and his grandfather in the churchyard at Frome. The sun was just rising and to the east the sky was glowing red and orange and gold. They had come to say goodbye to their grandfather's much loved friend, Thomas Ken, Bishop of Bath and Wells, who had died a few days before.

'He was a good man,' said his grandfather.

'And a brave one,' added his father.

'Will you tell me more about him, grandfather?' asked Thomas.

'When we get home, I will. After all you are named after him!'

So now they sat, the three of them, under the spreading branches of a huge cedar tree on the Vicarage lawn.

'I first met Thomas Ken when I was at school at Winchester College and he was chaplain. He'd been at school there himself and was proud to point out the initials that he had carved on a wall in the cloisters: "Tho. Ken 1656". He said it had taken him a long time because he had to work on it when no one was around!

'His family came from Somerset you know. They lived for hundreds of years at Kenn near Clevedon and that's how they got their surname.

'When Ken was chaplain he was such fun and so easy to talk

to. He loved music and sang and played the lute at parties. And he knew a lot about fishing. I think he got that from his half-sister, Anne's, husband, Izaak Walton who wrote a book about fishing called *The Compleat Angler*. Izaak was a wise and gentle man and Ken told me that he learnt a lot from him.

His mother and father had died when he was young so Anne and Izaak brought him up. He had a very happy childhood.

'While I was at Winchester he wrote some prayers for pupils to use. And he was the person who encouraged me to become a priest. I didn't see him again until 1685 and by then he was mixing with royalty and had been given many important jobs to do.

'I remember that in January 1685 Ken was in London and it was announced that he had been made Bishop of Bath and Wells. I was very pleased.

'King Charles II was a great admirer of Ken who stood up to him and warned him that some of the things that he was doing were wrong. Charles had a wife but he also had a friend, Nell Gwynn, and when they visited Winchester together Ken wouldn't allow Nell to stay in his house. Charles always remembered this but was not angry. He knew Ken was right. Once when Ken was giving a sermon at the Palace of Whitehall Charles said: "I must go and hear little Ken tell me of my faults."

'The king was quite ill by the time he had to appoint a new bishop for Bath and Wells. Several names were put to him but he made his own choice. "Od's fish!" he said. "Who shall have Bath and Wells but the little dark fellow who would not give poor Nelly a lodging!" Soon after as Charles II was dying, Bishop Ken, as he was by then, was sent for to say prayers at the king's bedside.'

'Od's fish! Od's fish!' interrupted Thomas. 'What a funny thing to say!'

'The king was always saying it,' laughed his grandfather, 'but you're not to say it. It's an oath and it means "God's flesh; the Body of Christ."'

'Now going back to 1685. In April James II was crowned king. As Bishop of Bath and Wells, Ken had to take part in the coronation ceremony at Westminster Abbey. He liked James but was afraid he wouldn't make a good king. James was a staunch Roman Catholic while England was Protestant and Ken could see trouble ahead.'

'And within a few days the trouble had started,' said John. 'I remember it well. Charles II's natural son, the Duke of Monmouth, decided he wanted to be king in the place of James II. He landed with an army at Lyme Regis and marched up into Somerset collecting men and money as he went. He was a Protestant and knew many people didn't want a Roman Catholic king.

'People hurried to join him. Some knew what they were doing. They supported the Protestant cause and were trained soldiers with muskets, ready to fight. Others were just caught up in the excitement and grabbed the nearest weapon they could find, maybe a pitchfork or a scythe, and joined the march.

'James II sent his troops to fight the rebels and the two sides met up on the Levels at Sedgemoor. Monmouth's men were no match for the King's army and many rebels were killed or taken prisoner.

'Monmouth himself was captured and imprisoned in the Tower of London. The King would not forgive him and he was

beheaded. Bishop Ken was with him the night before he died encouraging him to confess that he was guilty. The next morning Ken stood with Monmouth near the scaffold praying that God would forgive him. There was a huge crowd watching!

'It took five blows with the axe to cut off Monmouth's head.'

'Oh,' cried Thomas. 'That must have been horrible!' and he rubbed the back of his neck in sympathy.

'I'm sure it was,' said his father.

'Bishop Ken returned to Wells. He visited and comforted the prisoners. Some were chained in the cathedral cloisters with no food and no one to tend their wounds.

'Then Judge Jeffreys arrived to try the prisoners. He showed no pity and 99 men were sentenced to death in Wells. One was let off but the rest were hung, drawn and quartered. Many others were transported – sent overseas – to work in the sugar plantations in the Barbados. And some are still there, 25 years later.'

'But I remember when the Bishop came to visit us in the parish,' said John after a moment. 'You were so excited, father, when you got the message saying he was coming.'

'And so I was and so glad to see him again.'

'He visited the parish and stayed here with us,' went on John. 'We sat and talked under this same tree. He walked through the village talking to everyone especially the children. He was pleased that so many of them came to church and said their prayers each day.

He said that in some villages the people had forgotten how to pray. Then before he left he confirmed many of the children, including me.

'He was always so kind to the poor. It was said that he never passed a beggar in the street without giving them a coin and a blessing.

'And every Sunday when he was at the Palace in Wells he would invite twelve poor men and women to a good dinner and then he sent them home with all the leftovers for their families.'

There was a pause and then my grandfather continued: 'Sadly he didn't stay long at Wells. Bishop Ken always spoke the truth and kept his promises. He was not afraid of anyone,

however important and sometimes this got him into trouble.

'First he, and six other bishops, refused to obey James II and read a Declaration in church allowing people to worship as they liked. This was because it was against a law passed by Parliament. The bishops were imprisoned for a week in the Tower of London charged with rebellion. But a court and jury declared them not guilty.

'Not long afterwards some people invited James' daughter, Mary, and her Protestant husband William of Orange, to take over as Queen and King. James fled to France. But Bishop Ken supported James. He said that he had promised loyalty to James II and couldn't break his promise and accept William as king while James was still alive.

'He and six other bishops who said the same were forbidden to work and their jobs, houses and incomes were taken away. Thomas Ken could no longer work as a bishop and he had to leave the palace at Wells.

'An old friend of his, Tom Thynne, who lived at Longleat, invited Ken to make his home there and Bishop Ken lived there for the rest of his life. He spent the time reading and praying, visiting friends and writing letters and poems. I used to visit him sometimes and we would talk over the old days. I shall miss him a great deal.'

'But I shall always remember the stories about him,' said Thomas, 'and that you named me after him.'

# THE TALE OF THE GALLERY QUIRE

When I was a young lad I really hated going to church. It was cold and gloomy in the huge stone building, even in summer, and the parson droned on and on. We sat on hard benches in wooden boxes with high walls. I could only see the parson when I stood on a hassock or when he went up into the pulpit to preach.

It was all right for the squire. He had a grand box pew with comfy cushions and a fireplace. In the winter his servants lit a blazing fire to keep the family warm!

The parson preached for such a long time. He had an hour-glass beside the pulpit to tell him when an hour was up. We watched the sand trickle through the glass and longed for it to fill the bottom globe.

Once, when the sand had run from the top of the glass to the bottom the parson reached out and turned it over and prepared to go on with his sermon. But the clerk was too quick for him.

'Amen,' he said very loudly. 'Amen! Now we shall sing Psalm 100.'

The singing was miserable as well. We had no musicians – the old singers had gone to join the chapel – and we just sang the same old mournful tunes over and over again.

I longed to join the bigger boys who slipped out of church during the sermon and played amongst the tombstones. But my mother kept a firm grip on my arm if I tried to escape!

The best fun was when someone went to sleep and snored! The sexton would march up to them and rap them on the shoulder with his wand. They would wake up spluttering and snorting. And once the collie dogs from the Rectory farm rushed into church during the middle of the sermon, barking and chasing a cat! Everybody stopped listening and started laughing.

Then the old parson died.

The new parson was quite young and his sermons were shorter and sometimes even interesting.

'What we need,' he said, 'are some singers and musicians to lead the psalms.'

Next thing we knew, a huge wooden gallery was being built at the back of the church. It was very grand. It was coloured to look like marble and there was a painting of King David playing his harp on the front. A little staircase led up to the gallery.

The parson suggested that the musicians in the village band who played for parties should play the psalms in church as well. Some people didn't like that idea but the musicians did. My father, the village blacksmith, played the fiddle at parties and he was really keen. Especially when the churchwardens agreed to buy them some new instruments! A new bass viol, a fiddle, a clarinet and a flute were provided for the players.

But we still needed singers. The parson decided we needed a singing teacher. He invited James Ryal, a singing master who lived nearby, to come to our village to teach ten people to sing.  And I was one of them!  Just eight years old, I was very proud to be up in the gallery looking down on the heads of the congregation!

Mr Ryal brought his own book of tunes to teach us.  The musicians had their own tune books already with the dance tunes they played at parties.  They decided to copy the new psalm tunes into the backs of their books.  We boys learnt the top line of the music by ear and by heart.  And we sang our hearts out!

Now, thirty years on I'm still a musician in the gallery quire.  My father taught me to play the fiddle and I went with him to accompany the dancing at Harvest Home and Christmas parties.  I still do although he's too frail to play himself now.

All the older men who first sang in the church gallery are gone now and recently we decided that we needed some youngsters to join us.  A few weeks ago Christopher Alford from Mere became our new singing master.  We've already learnt some fresh tunes and are practising a long anthem to sing on Easter Day.  There are some fine solos and a very lively chorus, 'Alleluia!  Praise the Lord!' which gets faster and faster and louder and louder until the final Amen.  I think it's the best thing we've ever sung!

My two lads have joined the singers and there's some talk of girls singing too!  We'll see about that though!

Last Sunday Mr Alford suggested to the parson that when we sing a psalm the congregation should stand up, turn round and face the singers in the gallery.  'Facing the music,' it's called.  It certainly encourages the congregation to join in with

the singing and it feels quite cosy!

When it came to Easter Day the church was packed. The squire's pew was full of his family and guests, the ladies all wearing fine new bonnets. The anthem went really well and after the service the parson and the squire's lady both said how much they had enjoyed the singing.

We were very pleased and that evening the quire held a party of its own to celebrate. We ate cold beef and plum pudding and drank cider and then danced and sang until the small hours.

The next day we heard that Cary singers have fallen out with their parson. He rebuked them publicly from the pulpit for not doing what he asked them to do. Let's hope that never happens here!

*This story is loosely based on entries in the churchwardens' accounts for Henstridge and Templecombe between 1720 and 1750. The illustration is based on a drawing of the musicians at Sutton Montis in 1827. The gallery is an amalgam of that at Carhampton and that at Stocklinch Magdalen. It was 1769 when Parson Woodforde, curate at Castle Cary, fell out with his singers.*

# THE TALE OF HANNAH MORE AND HER SCHOOL AT CHEDDAR

Mary turned as she reached the churchyard gate, waved goodbye to her friend, Jane, and then walked thoughtfully along the dusty road towards her house in the centre of the village.

A few weeks ago Jane had left her home in Cheddar and gone to live at the Big House. Her aunt looked after the squire's children and had arranged for Jane to help her in the nursery with the new baby. If she did well she might be allowed to stay and train as a nurserymaid.

Every week she was given permission to meet Mary for an hour and there was so much to tell of her new life at the manor. Mary was soon able to picture it: the large rooms and beautiful furniture – plenty of chairs for everyone … even for visitors! Jane had a tiny room of her own next to the nursery with a patchwork quilt on the bed and a tall cupboard where she could hang her clothes. And there was always plenty of good food, even for the servants.

It was very different from the cottage where Mary lived with her parents and six brothers and sisters. Well, five now because Jack, the eldest, had gone to work on a farm at Rodney Stoke and lived in, sharing the attic bedroom there with four other young labourers.

Mary thought that her family was quite lucky. Her father was a carter and they lived in a larger cottage than many of the villagers. There were three bedrooms – the two boys slept in one and she and her sisters in the other. The baby still slept in her parents' room. Downstairs there was just one living room. Water had to be pumped from the well and heated over the open fire and it was often very smoky. The privy was at the bottom of the garden and Mary hated going there in the winter in the dark.

Her mother did her best to feed the family but it was always a struggle. Money was short even though she and the two boys took on work at the farm at busy times. The boys helped keep the birds off the crops and there was work for them all at harvest time. Mary stayed at home to look after the baby and her younger sisters.

Jane could hardly stop talking about the family at the Big House. There were seven children there including the new baby.

'John's the eldest. He's twelve. Then there's Margaret, Caroline, Arthur, the twins, George and Joanna, and the baby's called Frederick. John's going away to school soon. And there's a governess who teaches the older children. They can read and write and even know a very old language called Latin. And they know so many stories about the olden days and far-off lands. There's a picture hanging in the nursery of a huge animal called an elephant!'

'How lucky they are,' Mary had said wistfully. 'How I wish I could learn to read and write. In some villages there are schools. I wish someone would start one here in Cheddar.'

'Aunt says I must learn to read so that I can read to the children,' answered Jane. 'She's going to help me and when I can read, then I'll help you.'

As she turned the corner Mary saw her mother looking out for her. She seemed very excited and hurried to meet her daughter.

'Mary! Mary! Such news,' she cried. 'Two ladies have been to the house! Real ladies on horseback riding sidesaddle like the squire's lady!

'They told me that they intend to start a school in the village on Sundays and they wanted to know if I would let my children attend.'

'Mother! What did you say?' asked Mary eagerly.

'I said that the two boys might go if they wished but that my eldest daughter longed to go to school and would be there on

the day it opened! They seemed very pleased and asked your name.'

Mary was speechless! She hugged her mother and then began to dance down the street to the cottage. 'I'm going to school! I'm going to learn to read!' she sang and all the neighbours looked out of their houses and laughed!

The two ladies were sisters, Mrs Hannah More and Miss Patty More. They had heard that there was no school in Cheddar and that it was a pretty rough place from their friend, William Wilberforce. William, while on a visit to the Mores, had walked over to Cheddar to see the Gorge. But instead of returning full of wonder at its beauty he had come back sad and angry because the people of Cheddar seemed so poor and nobody seemed bothered. There was no school, no parish priest and no one to care for people who were ill.

Hannah decided that she must do something to help and hit on the idea of holding a school on Sundays. But before she put her plans into effect she and her sister visited everyone in Cheddar. The farmers were not keen on the idea – they thought that if ordinary folk learnt to read they might also learn to answer back! Some of the parents thought the children should be paid for attending school but others, like Mary's mother, were really pleased that their children would have a chance to learn and better themselves.

The sisters bought a house where the schoolmistress would live and a nearby barn, which once housed oxen, was cleared and re-roofed to serve as a schoolroom. The sisters – and Mary – watched as the barn was cleaned thoroughly and benches and books carried in. A headmistress, Mrs Baber, was appointed with her daughter, Betsy, to help her.

At last the school was ready and it opened on Sunday 25 October 1789. Mary was there punctually on the very first day. It was the beginning of a new life for her!

At first so many children enrolled that there was hardly room for them all and new teachers had to be employed. They learnt to read from the Bible and the Book of Common Prayer, not easy books to start with, but Mary learnt very quickly. Each morning there were prayers and during the day the children were told bible stories and other tales with a moral but they didn't learn to write or to do sums. The girls were also taught to knit and Mary was so quick to learn that she completed a muffler for her father in time for Christmas. 'No cold ears for me now!' he laughed as he kissed her.

When they grew tired the children practised singing and learnt hymns and psalms to sing in church and school finished each Sunday with a service in church.

Pupils were expected to come to school with clean faces and hands much to the dismay of some of the boys! Mrs Baber expected them always to tell the truth and encouraged them to treat others as they would like to be treated themselves. At first a great many children came but the numbers soon dropped and the sisters decided that they needed to do something to encourage them.

Mary was surprised to be given a penny one Sunday because she had attended school punctually for four weeks. 'I don't need a penny,' she said. 'I love coming to school but I'll give it to my mother. She'll be glad of it.' One day Mrs More and Miss Patty turned up unexpectedly with gingerbread for all the children – most of them had never tasted anything so good before! At the end of her first year Mary was given a fine white calico apron while some other girls were given mobcaps. She was delighted and determined to keep it sparkling clean. Her mother suggested that she only wore it to school and Mary agreed. Each boy who had persevered and done well was rewarded with a hat, shirt and a pair of shoes!

The More sisters had started schools in several other Mendip villages and the high spot of the school year was the annual Feast for all the schools held out-of-doors in one of the Mendip beauty spots. It was a tremendous affair and when Mary described it to Jane, now training as a nurserymaid, she was quite jealous!

'It was amazing, Jane. There were about a thousand children there from nine different schools. Those who came from a long way travelled in carts decorated with greenery while other wagons brought servants and so much food: great roasts of beef, huge plum puddings, bread, hundreds of cakes and lots of cider which was all carried to the picnic site.

'When all the children had arrived at the meeting point we formed a long procession with a band at the front which seemed to play the same tune, 'God save the King', over and over again. The Boy of Best Character led the way, waving a flag and next came Miss Hannah and Miss Patty followed by all the teachers. Then came the children walking two by two. I was asked to keep an eye on the little ones from Cheddar.

'We eventually reached the picnic site, a huge circular area, and entered under an arch decorated with laurels. Then the children started to sing some of the hymns they'd learnt as they made their way to the grassy area set aside for each school. I helped all our Cheddar children find somewhere to sit down. It was such a lovely day and the grass was springy and dry to sit on. Then a clergyman said grace and we were served with platefuls of wonderful food! More than we'd eat in a week in winter!

'After that we all recited passages from the Bible that we'd learnt by heart and sang some more hymns before forming up into our procession and singing 'God save the King' all together.' Mary fell silent.

'And what then?' asked Jane.

'I can't explain just how wonderful it was, all being together,' replied Mary. 'I was so happy that I wanted to cry!'

'I wish I'd been there too,' sighed Jane.

'But I've another piece of news,' said Mary, 'that I've been saving up to tell you. You know that Mrs Baber decided that I should learn to write as well as read. I've been offered a position as an assistant teacher at the Sunday School and Miss Hannah is going to help me to train as a full-time teacher in a day school.'

Jane hugged her friend. 'That is such good news. Who would have believed it! You a teacher and me a nurserymaid! Dreams really do come true!'

# BISHOP JIM AND A THOUGHT FOR THE DAY

When Bishop Jim Thompson was Bishop of Bath and Wells in
the 1990s, he often presented his 'Thought for the Day' on the
Today programme on Radio 4, usually from the studio but
once from a phone box with all the lorries roaring past! He
always began by saying 'Good Morning' and whether he was
talking about the environment or children or some world
catastrophe he was always able to demonstrate the presence
of God within the situation.

I have a book of Bishop Jim's 'Thoughts' and see that in 1994
he wrote one called Wells Springs. Sitting in the garden at the
Palace at Wells he watched the water springing up and
cascading over a waterfall into the moat and remembered how
Bishop Bekynton had provided a water supply from the same
spring for the people of Wells in 1450.

Bishop Jim was speaking on United Nations World Day of Water and remembered that in the world two billion people lacked safe water to drink; 25,000 children died daily from water-related diseases, and often women and children had to walk miles in blazing heat to fetch their basic water supply. 'It's a matter of life or death,' he said. 'Bishop Bekynton provided clean water for the people of Wells in 1450. Can we provide it for the world by 2000?' he asked.

The Bishop went on to remind us that the Bible was mostly written in a very hot, dry climate and water was often used to describe the blessing of God.

And that brings me back to the Big Drips in this book: each one in its own way helping to bring God's blessing to the people of Somerset.